Poems From Essex

Edited By Wendy Laws

First published in Great Britain in 2018 by:

 Young**Writers**

Young Writers
Remus House
Coltsfoot Drive
Peterborough
PE2 9BF
Telephone: 01733 890066
Website: www.youngwriters.co.uk

FOREWORD

Young Writers was established in 1991, dedicated to encouraging reading and creative writing in young people. Our nationwide writing initiatives are designed to inspire ideas and give pupils the incentive to write, and in turn develop literacy skills and confidence, whilst participating in a fun, imaginative activity.

Few things are more encouraging for the aspiring writer than seeing their own work in print, so we are proud that our anthologies are able to give young authors this unique sense of confidence and pride in their abilities.

For our latest competition, Rhymecraft, primary school pupils were asked to enter a land of poetry where they used poetic techniques such as rhyme, simile and alliteration to bring their ideas to life. The result is an entertaining and imaginative anthology which will make a charming keepsake for years to come.

Each poem showcases the creativity and talent of these budding new writers as they learn the skills of writing, and we hope you are as entertained by them as we are.

CONTENTS

Drapers Brookside Junior School, Harold Hill

Brooke Middleton (10)	66
Kacey Swanwick (10)	68
Chelsea Ben-Charles (10)	69
Aimee Chamberlain (10)	70
Mark Waterman (11)	71
Amy Trinder (11)	72

Five Elms Primary School, Dagenham

Lorinda Dajci (9)	73
Memunat Agaba (11)	74
Joshua Suraj Singh (10)	75
Reggie Sampson (10)	76
Mason Lynden Price (10)	77
Taylin Mehmet (10)	78
Amadu Balde (10)	79
Dylan Akash Singh (8)	80
Trisha Jannath (9)	81
Moeez Musharaf (10)	82
Jennifer Deativo (9)	83
Ruby Thomas (10)	84
Thai Wakeman (8)	85
Uririoghene Naomi Eweye-Emakpose (10)	86
Warishah Fatima (9)	87
Lexie Richardson (7)	88
Bhuvan Kirupaharan (10)	89

Gidea Park Primary School, Gidea Park

Isla Houston (9)	90
Abigail Ajose (9)	92
Jesse Goddard (8)	94
Katie Mann (8)	96
Mia Alger (9)	98
George Hines (9)	100
Lucy Alice McDermott (8)	102
Lexi Marcou (8)	104
Evita Backyte (9)	106
Carys Hayward (8)	108

Ethan Hambleton (8)	110
George Winser-Shead (8)	111
Hannah Jayne Wood-Murphy (9)	112
Siana Vandra (9)	113
Gregory Todorov (9)	114
Faizan Waseem Butt (8)	115
Daisy Holmes (9)	116
James Weston (9)	117
Jed Madunagu (8)	118
Grace Hersey (8)	119
Bradley Waddup (8)	120
Mia Josephine Moore (9)	122
Yasmin Cavanagh (8)	123
Henry Myles-Hook (9)	124
Connor Marks-Swain (9)	125
Dylan Legeai (9)	126
Bethany Norris (9)	127
Reyhana Ahmed (8)	128
Christian Hayes (8)	130
Malachi N'lemvo (9)	131
Tom Atkinson (8)	132
Erica Parker-Thomson (8)	133
James Martin (9)	134
Brooke Allen (9)	135
Viren Parmar (9)	136
Kamile Lapuskatie (9)	137
Jacob Farrell (8)	138
Kai Hindocha (8)	139
Roxy Ward (9)	140
Oliver Lucas (8)	141
Felix McKenzie Mason (9)	142
Bader Muftah (8)	143

Purfleet Primary Academy, Purfleet

Marvelous Daniel Ifeanyi (10)	144
Maia Phelut (9)	146
Charlotte Joanne Millard (9)	147
Priscilla Inyang (9)	148
Ogenna Ezeoke (9)	149
Kacey Riley (9)	150

Enoch Oluwatobiloba Akinwunmi-Taylor (8)   151

Daniella Dada (8)   152

Silver End Academy, Silver End

Ellen Mitchell (8)   153
Harmony Nicola Jane West (10)   154
Tyler Howlett (10)   155
Grace Aspinall (10)   156
Christopher Stephens (11)   157
Harriet Keeble (8)   158
Marcus John Harris (9)   159
Lia Reed (10)   160
Caitlyn Turner (11)   161
Megan Walker (11)   162
Lola Rees-Tearle (9)   163
Jasmin Perkins (11)   164
Lewis Plumer (9)   165
Max Moore (8)   166

THE POEMS

Gaming Land

Gaming Land is the place to be,
The characters you can see
Will hypnotise your eyes.
Will you see the fish that flies
Or a talking chair,
Or maybe a half-car, half-bear?
It's up to your controller,
The made-up champ bowler.
You could fight a monster
Or be a champ boxer.
Come children take charge,
This opportunity is large,
Honestly no need to barge.
Just head in the portal,
No need to be immortal.
Let your dreams take flight,
'Cause our light's so bright.

Eliana Tofunmi Fakokunde (9)

I Love My Game In Rhymecraft

My favourite game is Minecraft!
I want to write in Rhymecraft!

You start with nothing but a map.
You can start mining for an axe.

You find some coal
And make a torch.

You need some bricks.
We have to use some tricks.

My favourite game is Minecraft!
I want to write in Rhymecraft!

Ali Sakhi Shah (10)

It Turned Into...

Once upon a time, I caught a little rhyme.
I set it on the floor but it ran right to the door,
I chased it on a boat but it turned into a goat,
I chased it on a ferry but it turned into a berry,
I collected it in my hat but it turned into a cat,
I caught it by the tail but it turned into a whale,
I drew it on paper but it turned into a skyscraper,
I chased it on my bicycle but it turned into an icicle,
I set it on fire but it turned into a big fat liar,
I ate some ice but it turned into a plate of rice,
I got a dish but it turned into a big fish,
I had some hope but it turned into pink soap,
I had a tissue but it turned into a big issue,
I had a hot-air balloon but it turned into a raccoon,
I had a bottle of Fanta but it turned into Santa,
I chased it in my car but it turned into a chocolate bar!

Abiha Ali (6)
Aldborough Primary School, Ilford

Book City Siege

Self-Help book was enjoying his breakfast pulp
and ink,
Strangely, his newspaper stories began to shrink.
The radio flow was suddenly broken,
with an announcement of Book City stolen.
In shock, he jumped in fear of his beloved city,
What fate would befall from whose enmity?

He feared for his life, he feared for his identity.
In Book City, you're free to be whoever you want
to be
And travel without any ID.
In Book City you won't be searched to see what
magic you behold,
Neither would you be criticised young or old.
You could be whatever genre or size,
Without being force-fed fake news and lies.
In Book City it does not matter whether you are
rich or poor,
Through the glass ceiling you can soar.
Be black, be white,
Be any colour you like.

In Book City all were grateful and content,
Happiness you could share, own or rent.

But the view outside left Self-Help book aghast,
All the books were indeed becoming very unjust.
They were drained of thought and colour,
I say they had never looked duller.
Mental health seemingly was also an issue.
For all the books carried a pack of tissues,
Always crying, always depressed,
They were not feeling their best.
They walked around like zombies, totally unaware,
As if in the world they had not a single care.
The books could no longer read one another,
And feared Orwell's state of *'Big Brother'*.
Mr Dictionary had no meaning
And even the sun had stopped beaming.

Immediately Self-Help book knew what was
happening.
In fact, of the situation, he knew everything.
The 'Terminating Ten' were in town.
On the faces of all books they plastered frowns.

Facebook planted explosives in all the books.
Then masqueraded with emojis and fake looks.
Netflix, made all the books stare and stare and
stare,
Into nothing but thin air.
Snapchat put the books on selfie rampages
But the selfies showed nothing but blank pages.
Twitter stole words and cut them up,
Then left with a simple 'sup.
Whatsapp made all the books argue and fight,
Creating such a horrendous sight.
Along with venomous allies:
Instagram, Viber and YouTube obviously,
Candy Crush and don't forget music.lly.

Self-Help book was alone and in danger of being
captured,
And oh, how his heart was fractured.
Book City needs you.
They need your help, they really do!
Cut the power, cut the source, pull the wifi,
So the 'Terminating Ten' die.
Go and round up your army,

Grab Matilda, James and Charlie.
Call your friends, call your family,
Put an end to this calamity.
Read a book to save Book City!

Camilla Jannat Husain (10)
Aldborough Primary School, Ilford

A Book

A book is a mystical thing you see,
Take a leap into what you fancy,
Horror, fantasy, history and comedy,
Crime, romance, thriller, mystery, adventure or
murder.
The old magic lurks within,
Your characteristics will become a big
responsibility
For you will help the community, but who knows
You could cause a lot of mischief.
A book is a mystical thing you see
Take a leap into whatever you fancy.

A book is a mystical thing you see
Take a leap into whatever you fancy.
Pick wisely I would say
From demons to dungeons, to 1960 slaves,
A criminal escaping jail (though I hope you are
not),
For the full experience, you will see
From swinging with monkeys to climbing trees
The magic lurks within.

A book is a mystical thing you see
Take a leap inside whatever you fancy.

A book is a mystical thing you see
Take a leap inside whatever you fancy.
There are three cities you have to pass through,
The beginning is the most wonderful feeling,
Your story begins, your quest starts,
Middle, a problem starts,
Everyone starts to get worried or scared.
End, you have made it, the civilians rejoice in you,
A book is a mystical thing you see
Take a leap into whatever you fancy.

Kache Nimeshi Nguzo (11)
Aldborough Primary School, Ilford

The Nightmare Land

In your worst and horrible nightmare, the curse
has begun,
When you enter the land it will suck out all the fun,
When the ground starts to shake everyone will run
in fright,
This will all happen on a full moon
and horrific night,
When the entire light rises, the vampires will
ascend from their graves,
Trying to suck out all your blood, no one will
be brave,
The petrifying curse will go around the land
making people fall,
Then the zombies from the dead will stand
very tall.
When you enter the land, the cries of the bats will
spook you out,
"Argh!" you will say as you start to shout,
The hills on the land are a symbol of death
and blood,
Everybody will run away as they witness the flood,

Before you leave, the people of the dead will have won,
As the night of the curse will be over and done,
Enter the land if you dare
As the population is very rare.

Muhammed-Numan Faisal (10)

Aldborough Primary School, Ilford

Springtime

Hello spring, it's me...
Hello spring, it's Abbi...
I was calling from the other side
To tell you what I feel inside...
But now you're here
I have so much to share.

I planted some seeds in a box just for you,
They have little leaves that look new.
My little plants are springing...
"Mummy look! That one is flowering!"

In my garden, the daffodils and tulips have a
special colouring.
The cherry blossoms too, are flowering.
It smells like perfume in the air
And the ground is not so bare.

Spring, you make me so happy...
I am going to buy some more plants with Mummy.

My school projects are going to be more colourful
With lots of flowers to make them beautiful...

Thank you spring!
I can hear the birds sing.
It's not cold anymore...
Me and Mummy are going to the lake to explore.

Abigail Keen (8)
Aldborough Primary School, Ilford

Pokéland

P okémon work with humans, to get things done,
O ver the time they do it, they add a little fun!
K akuna, the bug-type Pokémon, busy in its shell,
É very day, wild Pokémon, making your life well,
L istening, learning, Pokémon, easily evolve
A nd everyone together will have problems they can solve!
N othing in Pokéland is ever bad,
D oing things together will help avoid being sad!

I n Pokéland it is always sunny,
S low and sticky is the rain, it rains honey!

E very geographical feature,
P okémon live in, unique little creatures!
I nside, outside, wherever you can find,
C ool, crazy Pokémon roam the land.

Yunus Khan (9)
Aldborough Primary School, Ilford

Unicorn Land

There's a big word in a little city.
The unicorns that live here look pretty.
There's a rainbow river
Where gummy snakes can slither.
Come and visit this place
Where you can stuff your face
In rainbow rivers.
There's a rainbow candy slide
Where you can glide on the slide.
The trees are green
But they're filled with cream.
A beautiful, enchantingly pure,
As white as a lily, so proud and sure
With a silvery mane that flows in the breeze
And eyes that bewitch you
And make your soul freeze,
But in an instant
The unicorn's eyes seem to change
And so melts the ice causing feelings strange.
Straight to your heart, the warmth travels but slow
And both captive and unicorn seem to shine and
glow.

Hania Naqvi (7)
Aldborough Primary School, Ilford

Cold And Icy Land

C is for cold Christmas that everyone enjoys

O is for outstanding snow slowly melting

L is for lovely lakes frozen

D is for the ducks on the frozen lakes

A is for the advent calendar that you open every
    day

N is for not being naughty or no presents

D is for the deer that moves Santa's sleigh

I is for the icicles that fall on your head

C is for Christmas which is cold

Y is for the young children that love Christmas

L is for lights that light up your Christmas tree

A is for the antler that reindeer have

N is for the nights before Christmas

D is for deer that move Santa's sleigh.

Ashvin Shanti Kotecha (9)

Aldborough Primary School, Ilford

The Rat Of The Highway

The Rat of the Highway is a bad stealer.
His land is made of food but it's gone now!
He can taste all of the succulent, chocolatey jam
cake with velvet on top.
He eats caramel, makes it stick,
Puts it on brioche.
He eats chocolate apples, eats pineapples,
Goes as fast as a cow
And speaks like a cat who... miaows!
He's always sunny
And the best thing about him is he's funny.
Oh golly, what can he do?
Smell, taste, see, hear, touch
But there isn't any food left.
He's very crazy and always likes being lazy.
He saw some yummy grass
But the other animals ate all of it.
He hears the jammy waterfall made out of bread
But he's tired so he has a nap!

Amara Christine (6)
Aldborough Primary School, Ilford

Music Central

I can see music notes shining like the sun's rays,
Instruments, crowding streets and buildings.
People tapping their feet to random melodies,
But are somehow able to synchronise in perfect
harmony.

No corner is silent, but instead filled with musical
song,
Choruses and melodies buzzing through the air.
A person's steps but to others a drumbeat,
Creative waves flowing like the ocean.

A person's scream, but to others a ghoulish song,
Playing on eternal repeat.
Every sentence is a melodic phrase,
Each house a separate song.

Everything, everyone and everybody,
Different in each way possible,
But all living in the endless chaos,
Called Music Central.

Hiba Shaukat (11)
Aldborough Primary School, Ilford

Halloween

It was a dark and gloomy day
But some people were dressed in hay.
On a Halloween night watch out,
Before the goblin attacks without a clue.
This is a season for ghost stories,
Monsters, tricks and frights.
When witches fly across the moon
You know Halloween is coming soon.
Lock your doors and turn out the lights,
The ghosts and goblins will spook you with a fright.
May the tricks that you asked to do
Be a trick to help you gain a friend or two.
So, by tomorrow, pick three friends
And give them all a Halloween treat.
We're stuffed with cakes and candy,
We had a lot of fun.
But now it's time to go to bed
And dream about all the things we've done!

Hurrea Ali (10)
Aldborough Primary School, Ilford

The Rainbow World

Tiny speckles in the sky,
Not a word, nor hello or goodbye,
I speak out loud,
Through the cloud,
Just so someone can hear me.

I close my eyes to colours so bright,
A rainbow filled land so barely in sight,
Telescopic powers,
Tall, towering flowers,
A tingle of excitement from what I see.

A reality or a dream,
Makes me want to scream,
A place so cool
And I'm stuck in school.
Shhh... a hypnotic rainbow world it must be!

Happy, peaceful, pretty and calm,
Reflections of white daisies in my palm,
I want to go there, not a minute to spare,
My friend, let's not stay here,
An amazing, awesome adventure is the key!

Aaliyah Mir (9)
Aldborough Primary School, Ilford

Beauty Unicorn

B eauty is worth the waiting for
E verything has beauty
A nemones shimmer in the sun
U ses water in crystal jewels, on the ground
T he beauty unicorn brings beauty in every life
Y ou will fall in love with Beauty.

U nicorns shimmer all over the land
N othing beats the glimmering, sparkling sand
I ce dazzles and dances in the sky
C lips to dresses to sparkling jewellery
O ceans to rivers dazzle while you see your clear reflection
R ings scatter all over the land
N othing can beat inner beauty and make-up
S himmering stars are like jewels in the night.

Sara Ahmed (9)
Aldborough Primary School, Ilford

Creepy Land

Creepy, creepy cave, why is it so dark?
Maybe there is a humongous shark.
Argh! This is terrible
As people say it's horrible.

I really need a chance to look
Because I'm looking for a place to cook.
What! Look, there is a train,
OMG it is starting to rain.

You will need to move
As you will face your doom.
Why are you going up?
Now I will turn you into a cup.

I am cold, I need a sock
This is even worse but I'm shocked.
I need help,
Just not from a Celt.

Look over there, it is a lolly
And look there is something rolling.

Ouch, I have a sugar rush,
Now I feel like a brush.

Rukayya Ali (10)
Aldborough Primary School, Ilford

The Cursed Island!

As soon as you enter the cursed island
A spooky shiver will run down your spine,
Vampires, witches and all of those things
Will rise from the dead and come from behind.

Watch out! Fire-breathing dragons fly over your heads,
As you look around you'll realise the sky is red,
Wolves attack,
Together in a pack.

The rivers are ice,
Falling into it won't be nice.
You'll turn around to run back,
The journey will be petrifying and that's a fact.

This island may sound the worst,
But that is only because it is under a curse!
It waits for its hero to come,
For this island will change back to being fun!

Sumaya Miah (11)
Aldborough Primary School, Ilford

The Land Of Spring

Spring, the sweet spring
Is now this year's new king.
The green grass will begin to grow
And replace white winter's snow.

The time has come, for golden daffodils to bloom,
Across the sky, speedy planes zoom.
Little white lambs frisk and play,
They love to play, they play, all day.

Beside the lake, beneath the trees,
Butterflies fluttering in the cool breeze.
Lambs run around dancing and prancing,
As larks perch on dark brown branches.

As shafts of delicious sunlight strike to the floor,
Everyone opens spring's new door!
The mist turns from white to gold,
Spring itself is starting to unfold.

Damanpreet Kaur (11)
Aldborough Primary School, Ilford

A Place

Have you ever wondered about a place
Where you could stuff your face
And where amazing things come true?
And if you don't believe it bring a mirror
And watch your face turn from red to blue.

Watch the river which is shining bright
And have a sample of chocolate delight
Or eat tree cream,
It's like a dream
And watch the flavoured rainbow pass by,
Dashing and whizzing across the sky.

Have you ever wondered about a place
Where you could longingly stuff your face
Infinitely around the place?
Look around at the shining bright
And have a taste of everlasting delight.

Yusuf Butt (9)
Aldborough Primary School, Ilford

Toffee Land

Toffee apples, toffee lollipops and so much more,
All things are made of toffee to the core!

Welcome to Toffee Land,
Over here, come and buy a toffee hand
Or perhaps you'd prefer a toffee sweet,
Either way, it'll be a real treat!

Toffee apples, toffee lollipops and so much more,
This is a great place, that's for sure!

There's a stream of gooey toffee canes
And toffee on all window panes.
If you take a look around
You'll surely know, it's Toffee Town.

Toffee apples, toffee lollipops and so much more,
So many tantalising treats to explore!

Brisa Dwivedi (10)
Aldborough Primary School, Ilford

Never Turn Your Back

In a dark night I saw a haunted house,
To and fro there was a running mouse.

Some bats were flying in the sky,
It's scary, spine-chilling and it made me fry.

The enormous door was opened wide
And skeletons were dancing inside.

We entered the house and held our breath
And a tarantula bounced on our heads.

The skeletons were inviting us to dance with them,
But don't worry if they make you lame.

We ran to come out all,
From behind ghosts were giving calls.

At last we saved our souls,
The night is darker, whoo-hoo is the sound of the owl.

Jawad Faruque (11)
Aldborough Primary School, Ilford

Candy Life

Candy cane, candy cane,
Jelly beans, very sweet.
There are candy people, delicious,
Appetising, ready to eat.
I never need to bake,
I live in a house full of mouth-watering fudge cake.
On the south of Candy Cane Lane
Yummy milkshake lake,
Rock candy sugar, sweet never sandy,
Be prepared to climb,
Eat, nothing will beat,
Mountain, marshmallow,
Train softer than a pillowcase.
Jelly beans make it rain,
Drives gingerbread children insane.
I am walking home licking my chocolate road
That never gets old,
Oh, what's that I see?
A gummy trampoline, yummy.

Reauna Stuart-Jemmott (11)
Aldborough Primary School, Ilford

Plants Vs Zombies

P unched by a bonk choy

L ittle imps are fast but not strong

A dd some plants to your life

N o more zombies!

T oo many zombies!

S pike rock is the strongest plant.

V ery active and exotic plants

S uper strong walnuts.

Z ombies are losers

O h no! Please don't eat our brains

M y plants are better than you

B ut the only thing that is bad is the Boss Level

I can see the zombies and they're coming

E at your brains

S lapped by a celery stick.

Faizaan Goga (8)
Aldborough Primary School, Ilford

The Land Of The Dead

Where skeletons walk
And the ghosts talk,
This is the Land of the Dead.

Where the souls are loose and free
And so clear that you can see,
This is the Land of the Dead.

Where spirits wander around
Without making any sound,
This is the Land of the Dead.

Where skeleton children play all day
And the parents have nothing to say,
This is the Land of the Dead.

Music is all you can hear
Which makes you want to cheer,
This is the Land of the Dead.

Music, spirits, souls,
This is the Land of the Dead.

Zarif Islam (11)
Aldborough Primary School, Ilford

Winter Nightmare Wonderland

One day there was a little girl called Monica,
She was singing along, la, la, la.
It was snowing at night in the Paris tower.
One day she heard something strange,
"Help, help."
She wanted to go
But the scared girl was in the forest
But she was very brave.
She went to save her but nobody was there.
Poof, she saw a creepy, scary clown
And a red balloon.
She knew who the clown was,
It was Pennywise.
George, all the creepers
And friendly Frouzzbear surrounded her.
I need to go and save her.
Run, run, run.

Roberto Popovici (8)
Aldborough Primary School, Ilford

Have You Been To A Football Pitch?

Have you ever been to a football pitch?
Have you ever been to a football pitch?
You have to go now, now, now!
I hope you go there, it's so much fun.
You'll get popcorn and a cold drink to munch.

See how the super strong goalies
Catch the ball and hear the victory glories.

If the match is over don't be sad and miserable.
Very soon the next match will bring lots of fun.
Now the match is over, go and see the beach
And cherish the memories of this pitch.

Please go and see the beach.
Please go and see the beach.

Vihaan Dange (7)
Aldborough Primary School, Ilford

The Sundae Adventure

I fought my way through the endless void of ice
cream.
I was in ecstasy...

Suddenly, my foot slipped,
I could hear the river below me,
The waves wrestling and jostling with each other.
They flew by carrying small gumballs,
Macaroons and billions of tiny sprinkles.

I finally released my grip
From the crumbling flake in-between my hands.
I was tired but relieved.

Plunging through the air,
I landed in the cascading river,
I was like a magnet being pulled by the current.
I was suddenly awake from my dream.

Isabella Topaz Allitt (10)
Aldborough Primary School, Ilford

Nightmare City

I wake up every night
To find that I'm not in my bed,
I'm standing in darkness
In my Nightmare City.
Past, present, future horrors,
Terrorising beasts and monsters,
Empty pitch-black silence surrounds me
In my Nightmare City.
My screams are drowning me,
Everywhere I turn I see shadows,
I'm choking on a thick layer of suspense,
In my Nightmare City.
I try to break the walls, but I can't find them,
I'm searching through an infinite path,
Stumbling over my own steps
In my Nightmare City.

Rija Shaukat (11)
Aldborough Primary School, Ilford

Every Day Is Christmas

Every day it's Christmas.
I hear children laughing and having lots of fun.
I also hear children opening presents.
My mum makes delicious dinner.
My cousins come to my house.
The first thing we do is play.
The next thing we do is have dinner.
When everyone has finished their dinner
We wait 10 minutes
And then we open our amazing presents.
I was screaming because I couldn't believe what I got.
It was what I always wanted.
Our Christmas tree was so big,
We also had an ornament when we were with Santa Claus.

Oliwia Kalesza (8)
Aldborough Primary School, Ilford

My Dream World

It's a wonderland of nature and music,
It is where you can do anything.
A land where mythological animals roam,
Somewhere you can be anything wherever you go.
A bizarre world of dreams and hopes,
For you can enter if you believe.
The opposite of evil
Where bad can't roam.
If you want to go somewhere where the darkness
doesn't roam,
Come to my dream world,
Though why?
Because...
It's music to my ears!
So enjoy my world I created beyond my
imagination!
It's fun! Come play!

Jessica Zheng (10)
Aldborough Primary School, Ilford

A Cool Place To Be!

Hills formed out of ice cream
With lollipop trees.
Houses made of gingerbread
Stuck together with cement.
Not just any cement, but caramel!
Squished within the chocolate bricks.

With flakes in the hills
And chocolate in the houses,
This is a place you can't miss,
I'd come here from afar, wouldn't you?
Added with a gummy nature,
It's like a sweet holiday!

Birds in the sky,
Rabbits on the ground.
This is a place
Where you can stuff your face!

Wareesha Asif (10)
Aldborough Primary School, Ilford

Candy Town!

Hi, welcome to Candy Town,
You will meet lots of funny clowns,
There are lots of candy sticks,
Everyone loves to lick,
This town is full of candyness,
When I go to the shops, I see happiness,
There are chocolate games,
But there are lots of names,
There is a chocolate river,
The gummy snakes can slither,
There is a candy house,
It is owned by a little mouse,
There is a lake,
You might find a snake,
You will have lots of dreams,
On the ceiling, there is cream.

Aarav Minhas (8)
Aldborough Primary School, Ilford

Melted Chunky Chocolate

Melted Chunky Chocolate is a land
Where you can eat everything,
The grass, the trees, plants and cars.
In this land there is a boy called Choc,
He's the only Choc in the land.
He's also made out of chocolate,
Lucky for him, nobody can eat him,
Otherwise, it would be a disaster for him!
Choc doesn't speak that much,
He's too shy.
I was talking about how you can eat anything,
Choc ate a giant, massive car,
And he ate half of the grass in the land.

Rishi Syed Ali (9)
Aldborough Primary School, Ilford

Slimy Land

As you walk in Slimy Land everything is slime,
There's no turning back or that's a crime.
Everyone there is called Vicky
Just because they're all so sticky.

It is so stinky
That it makes everyone wrinkly.
The smell is so strong
In school every answer you wrote was wrong.

When the sticky floor tries to pull you in,
Get out and try to win.
So remember if you go in there's no turning back,
So before you go in fetch a snack.

Mussa Chughtai (10)
Aldborough Primary School, Ilford

Popoland

Near my house we had a dream land,
This was called the 'Popoland'.
All it grew was papaya fruit
Making it a splendid photo shoot.

Yellow, yellow was the colour,
Which we could see forever and ever.
There was a bad man in the town,
He wanted to bring the Popoland down.

All the kids in town went to him,
Asked him not to make such a sin.
He changed his mind to not touch the land
Now we still have our 'Popoland'.

Samidha Prasad Pai (6)
Aldborough Primary School, Ilford

Candy Land

In caring Candy Land
Every single thing is grand.
It is all very nice,
It is free of price!
If you eat a candy cane
All your fears will drain.
Marshmallows, candyfloss clouds,
Makes everyone go loud!
Decorations will light up your day,
While you have fun on your sleigh!
Delicious mountains have ice cream,
Topped with sprinkles that are green.
Send a friend to Candy Land,
Where the magic of candy never ends.

Gloria Debnath (10)
Aldborough Primary School, Ilford

Dreams

Dreams can take you anywhere
Like a river of rainbows,
Clouds of candyfloss and gummy bears,
They can even take you to a whole new world,
Like a time machine,
The Great Fire of London,
Stone Age time.

There could even be some dangerous dreams like...
Knights battling dragons,
Going on adventures
To find new species of dragons,
Riding on a dragon's back.
Where will my dream take me today?

Rayhan Miah (9)
Aldborough Primary School, Ilford

Rainbow Land

R is for the Rainbow shimmering down on my face.

A is for the Awesome rays beaming from space.

I is for the Incredible colours we all embrace.

N is for the Natural shades of grace.

B is for the Beautiful bees flying around the rainbows on the chase.

O is for the Outstanding shape the rainbow creates to my eyes which is the case.

W is for the Wonderful world that creates the maze!

Shiane Luggah (9)

Aldborough Primary School, Ilford

Stories Of Football

Have you ever been to a football pitch?
I have.
Have you played football?
I have, so let's start playing.
One snowy, sunny day
I was playing football with my team
I was trying to score but I couldn't.
It was snowing and I arched my backbone.
My teammates said, "No!"
Because the others did a goal.
Their teammates' goalkeeper was clapping.
The shot was beautiful and brilliant.

Kartik Semwal (7)
Aldborough Primary School, Ilford

Apple

An apple a day
Keeps the doctor away.

It tastes sweet and yummy,
Fills up my hungry tummy.

Red, green, yellow, pink
Thinking about them makes my eyes wink.

Apple pie, apple sauce,
Need a coin to toss.

As soon as I ate an apple
I felt like a Prince Charming in a castle.

I wish I had thousands of seeds to sow
So that I can have lots of apples to grow.

Mayank Kamble (7)
Aldborough Primary School, Ilford

My Magical World

Welcome to my magical world
Where everything is made out of gold.

You can fly on my magical birds
And never get tired of their words.

Unicorns with their horns will be your friends.
You will never get tired of their hymns.

Fruits of every colour and taste
Will be at your gate.

Come to my magical land
I will be waiting for you in my golden crown.

Husna Sakhi (8)
Aldborough Primary School, Ilford

The Beast Of Autumn

The heart of autumn has arisen,
Colder it will get.
Red, yellow, orange and brown,
Colours that we will never forget.
Sometimes we'll get wet,
I just love this season.

The leaves are falling down,
Slowly everything is going
Like the circle of life,
Everyone is shouting
That we are celebrating,
Autumn, autumn, autumn,
Oh yeah, winter is tomorrow.

Amritpal Singh (10)
Aldborough Primary School, Ilford

Halloween

I'm excited, it's Halloween,
Everyone is dressed in spooky costumes.
I see children getting sweets.
I see houses decorated spookily.
I see children happy
Walking, on the way talking and talking.
It's dark and so scary,
Children looking as scary as skeletons
And some of them as a real ghost, *wooooooo*.
Happy Halloween.
Does this house have sweets?

Herman Kola (5)
Aldborough Primary School, Ilford

Sugar Life!

S weet Candy Land
U ncontrollable
G roomed sprinkles
A tasty world
R eally yummy.

Sugar is sweet.
Sugar is tasty.
Sugar is my life
Because I love pastry
Sugar is good.
Sugar is trusty.
Sugar is healthy.
Sugar is wealthy.
Sugar is white
Sugar is brown
Which one I eat, never let me down.

Prishay Janjua (7)
Aldborough Primary School, Ilford

Football World

F ootball is so cool

O n Football Land were Ronaldo, Messi and Naymar

O n it kids go playing football with their favourite football players

T all stadiums and people live in footballs

B ecause it is Football World

A nd in future you will see it

L eah has lived here for 30 years

L eo has lived here for 25 years.

Leah Monteiro-Chaytors (7)

Aldborough Primary School, Ilford

M&Ms Land

In M&Ms Land
There is no sand,
Everybody wears chocolate bands
On their chocolatey hands!

In M&Ms Land
Nothing is bland,
Choco balls are grand
And M&Ms are a brand!

In M&Ms Land
Sprouts are banned,
Orange M&Ms make you tanned
But best of all
The minute Skittles that are really small.

Imran Iftikharul Islam (10)
Aldborough Primary School, Ilford

Candy Cane Lane

Candy Cane Lane is fun,
I would love to eat a bun.

The people are good,
The houses are made out of wood.

I love the city,
It is so pretty.

My land has a caramel river,
It goes at a slither.

It's lots of fun,
But then it's all done.

The grass is green,
The people love cream.

Aroosh Asif (6)
Aldborough Primary School, Ilford

Cat Land

C ute City is the capital of Cat Land

A dorable Area is a cat amusement park

T ame Tunnel is an ancient artefact

L ittle Labyrinth is an old maze

A ttractive Alley is the tallest mountain in Cat Land

N oble Navy is the name of Cat Land's army

D andy Desert is a desert made by Catgyptians.

Ranveer Singh Shergill (8)
Aldborough Primary School, Ilford

Chocolate In Christmas

C hocolate milk being made

H ot chocolate in winter

O bstacles frozen solid

C rows pecking on water fountains

O bjects outside frozen

L akes frozen with thick ice

A ll tabby cats sitting in their warm beds

T ea drunk by parents

E verybody sleeping in their warm, cosy beds.

Paramjeet Kaur (8)

Aldborough Primary School, Ilford

Sweets And Chocolate

Sweets are unhealthy, if you eat too much
Your teeth become black,
They fall out and crack.
So do not eat too much.
I'm warning you not to eat too many sweets.
You should listen when your parents say no,
Do not eat sweets.
If they say yes you can eat sweets
Even chocolate.
Okay, listen to me, do not eat sweets.

Haadia Lawal (5)
Aldborough Primary School, Ilford

Candy Land!

In Candy Land there are lollipop trees
And a marshmallow city.
It looks so yummy
I want to take a peek.
In my dream I want to stay,
What a lovely place to play.
There's a rainbow candy slide,
What a surprise!
There's a lovely chocolate river
Where you can swim forever!

Syeda Areej Naqvi (9)
Aldborough Primary School, Ilford

The Magical Land Of Sweetness

S weetness is waiting

W ondrous places to visit too

E xcitement awaits

E at as much as you want

T astier than you think

N on-stop sugar

E njoy all you want

S it back and relax

S ugar, sugar here I come.

Tharuli Chenaya Thanthriarachchi (7)

Aldborough Primary School, Ilford

Candy Land

C ome and see my candy land

A nd it's a nice place with candies everywhere

N umerous varieties of candies to pick

D elicious chocolate fountains to lick

Y ou can enjoy yourself in Candy Land forever.

Keerthana Bharathi Raja (7)

Aldborough Primary School, Ilford

Money Land

M y land is made of money

O n the ranges of enchanting worlds

N one of the banks here to rob as in our world

E verything pops up from existing cash trees

Y es, there is your rich fortune growing here.

Dinesh Reddy Padala (10)

Aldborough Primary School, Ilford

Scrumptious Sweets

S crumptious, succulent sweets
W hich one shall I eat?
E ach one melts extremely slowly
E very time I am feeling lonely
T asty treats are yummy to suck
S o delicious, I never say yuck!

Safiyyah Bubulia (6)
Aldborough Primary School, Ilford

My Animal Land

Animal Land is paradise...

I can hear the birds chirping like sweet music
And deer hooves on the colourful paths.
I can see a fountain of rainbows
And otters bathing in it.
I can see a unicorn sanctuary and tiny piglets.
I can smell the summer air
And the Twiglet trees.
I can taste the marshmallow cupcakes
Melting in my mouth as I enjoy the gooey treat.
I can feel the soft, wavy grass on my knees
As I wander through the fields.

Animal Land is colourful and fun
And it's created by my imagination.

May Violet Cashman (9)
Cooks Spinney Academy & Nursery, Cooks Spinney

Candy Land

I can see the pink cotton candy unicorn
floating in the bright blue sky.
I can feel the soft, loving breeze swiftly going by.
I can taste the sweet and sour candy canes
popping on the green grass.
I can touch the sparkling chocolate fountain
spraying like fireworks.
I can hear the unicorns weaving through the
candy fields, stopping to take a bite.
Would you like to come?

Summer Ashleigh Harrison (10)
Cooks Spinney Academy & Nursery, Cooks Spinney

Crazy Land

My crazy land...

I feel the heat of the purple sun tanning
my shoulders.
I see the flying guitars playing sweetly like a bird.
I smell the sticky fudge pour from the chimneys
on top of the houses all around.
I taste fresh doughnuts from the Crazy
Land bakery.
I hear the pink raindrops falling into the
winding river.

Demi Lea Hughes (9)
Cooks Spinney Academy & Nursery, Cooks Spinney

Stingy The Stingray

Deep in the hidden depths of the majestic ocean
I live,
At the bottom of the sandy shores,
All the other fish above me
Swimming around like buzzy bees.

Be careful,
Don't tread on my tail!
If you feel something as flat as a pancake
While you're swimming around you have a nasty
surprise coming your way.

Sting! Sting! Sting!

I watch all the feral fish
Swimming above me, having fun,
Then there's me - solitary, wishing
I could be one of them.

I just swim on the bottom of the hidden seas,
Fearing that I will get eaten by my vicious prey!
Sometimes I'm so scared
I roll up into a ball like a hedgehog.

Down in the fantastic, enchanted forest
Full of magical creatures,
I look up above me
And see the king of the ocean floating above.
I have an extremely long tail,
Hoping that it comes in handy when I impale my prey...

I hear the waves of the sea,
Slamming against the shores, *whoosh!*
While I swim; like a snake slithering through
The damp jungle.

I see a mermaid swimming around
With blue and purple hair
Leaving a flair behind her.

Olly the octopus is daydreaming,
Meanwhile, Patrick the pink starfish is surfing tidal waves
While fish fight to eat burgers.

I am the stingray.

Brooke Middleton (10)

Drapers Brookside Junior School, Harold Hill

Potatoville

Every potato down in 'Potatoville' loved potatoes,
Potatoes loved potatoes,
Everybody gave each other hugs and kisses
Until one day...
The tomatoes came.
They invaded our hugs and kisses.
They invaded our homes.
They invaded the potatoes.
We all went to war.
Us potatoes had our chip swords,
Our potato helmets and everything!
The tomatoes just had a sword,
In the middle of that war between the tomatoes
And the potatoes, one of the tomatoes exploded.
Some of the tomato went on the potato's sword
And the potato tried it and he loved it,
He was so happy.
In the end, every potato and tomato were friends.

Kacey Swanwick (10)
Drapers Brookside Junior School, Harold Hill

A Magical Land

In a magical land
Everything looks grand,
All the unicorns are beautiful
And they are also magical.
There is lots of positivity
And a fun activity,
It's a place humans want to live
Because it's a place to give.

Fairies live there too,
One of them might be you,
I would rather make a wish
Rather than turning into a fish!
All their houses look so pretty,
It even looks like a city!
All the little sparkles glisten,
How about you give it a listen.

Chelsea Ben-Charles (10)
Drapers Brookside Junior School, Harold Hill

The Slithery Stingray

I live in the clear Paradise Ocean -
I slither along the sandy shore.

I am the shadow of sorcerous seas,
I camouflage into the silky sand
Hunting for ferocious prey.
I am fearful and frantic,
Searching through the depths
Of the sandy sea,
I am a snake slithering
Up the sheltered tree.

I can sting with my serpent-like tail
And my shadowy stomach that lays upon the
ground.

I am a stingray.

Aimee Chamberlain (10)

Drapers Brookside Junior School, Harold Hill

World Of Paper

The World of Paper
Starts off as dark and empty
But just wait and see...

The magic is real
In this world that you create
You choose its start and finish.

After a mistake
Has been made in paradise
You can erase it.

You can make it bright
You can make it colourful
Or it can be plain.

The World of Paper
Starts off as dark and empty
But just wait and see...

Mark Waterman (11)
Drapers Brookside Junior School, Harold Hill

Puppies' Kingdom

P ups can sing and dance all day
U nder the stars it's never grey
P ull it together we can sing forever
P ups can sing and dance together
I n the sky so high, a unicorn is passing by
E very time a pup sings everyone has to join in
S ing and dance all night until the sunrise...

Amy Trinder (11)
Drapers Brookside Junior School, Harold Hill

Untitled

On a lonely day on Minecraft
You may be sitting in a mineshaft.
Tired and bored,
You take out your sword.
You see mobs are nearby,
So you look closely with one eye.
Overtaken by fear,
You listen with your ear.
Nothing can be seen,
Only one thing can be heard.
"Footsteps," is the word.
Then you run through the hallways, getting lost,
Always you turn the corner and see a miner.
His eyes are white
And full of light.
You blink and he's gone.
By then it's dawn
And to this day, the legend lives,
Some may decline, to believe in Herobrine.
The truth, we may never know
But we can let the legend grow.

Lorinda Dajci (9)
Five Elms Primary School, Dagenham

Nature Nation

Nature Nation is a place of tranquillity,
A place to sit down and explore its creativity,
You'll marvel at the wondrous things you see,
Everything is set out so elegantly.

Dainty lush leaves
Sprout from sturdy oak trees,
That reflect in the crystal-clear waterfall,
It glistens when the sun smiles in a perfectly round
ball.

Don't forget the animals that live here happily,
They sing and run so cheerfully,
The exotic birds fly very early,
While the owls only come out rarely,
The butterflies flutter and the squirrels mutter.

Come and admire the creatures
And live in this nation's blissful features.

Memunat Agaba (11)
Five Elms Primary School, Dagenham

Ridiculous Rides!

Welcome, I'm Dr Zackinstein,
Let me introduce you to 'Ridiculous Rides'
Where you have to get up and don't be lazy,
I'm telling you the rides are crazy!

Come on, go on Twister Extreme,
It's impossible not to scream.

Rage goes up and loops-the-loop,
There's also a ride that will make you puke.

If you survive the ghost scream,
You will win some chocolate ice cream.

There are prizes to win on pick the ducky,
You will win a cuddly teddy if you're lucky.

Hope you enjoyed the ridiculous rides,
When you leave make sure you give me a high five.

Joshua Suraj Singh (10)
Five Elms Primary School, Dagenham

Dream Island

I had a dream I was in this land
With lots and lots of golden sand.
Great big trees, a forest I saw,
I swear there was a dinosaur.
I walked in the forest, walked on the green grass.
I saw a huge snake as it slithered past.
I came to an opening, my eyes drew big,
I saw a lollipop hanging off a twig.
Candy canes everywhere,
My mum wouldn't have let me but I don't care.
I reached up to get a sweet,
My head was racing, I could feel my heart beat.
I felt a hand grab hold of me,
Then I heard my mum's voice waking me up gently.

Reggie Sampson (10)
Five Elms Primary School, Dagenham

Dreams And Nightmares

In the world, everyone does it,
We all lie down and rest our head.
When we all get tired, we start to sleep
And then we get into bed.

We then luckily drift into Dream Land!
It's full of rainbows and magic,
You can befriend fish which can speak!
Most of all, you can tame a unicorn!
That's not tragic!

But if luck tears apart, we go to Nightmare Land!
It's full of spooks and scares,
With its monsters and beasts
It's known for its dares!

Be safe when sleeping from now on!

Mason Lynden Price (10)
Five Elms Primary School, Dagenham

Candy Land

In the world of Candy Land
I picked lots of sweets in my hand,
They were so tasteful and yummy,
It sure filled up my tummy.

It was filled with chocolates and sweets,
I gave myself some sugar beets.

I walked into a room full of cookies and cream,
I let out the biggest scream,
I have never seen anything like this,
They even had chocolate crisp,
I could hear lots of crackle and sizz,
I needed a drink, soda pop fizz.

Everything was so delicious and divine,
I wish it could all be mine.

Taylin Mehmet (10)
Five Elms Primary School, Dagenham

Rock Star Rhymes The Lime

Candy Land had a rock star.
The rock star had a hot car.
He was good at rhymes
But also needed lime.
One night there was a light,
He was making a concert,
But then his belly started hurting.
He asked his band to lend him a hand.
They ran home
And all they could find was a phone.
Then they just moaned.
Finally, they found the lime
And without a rhyme,
They were there in time.
The day was saved,
We shout hooray
But don't you worry
We'll be back in a hurry.

Amadu Balde (10)
Five Elms Primary School, Dagenham

Virtual Zoo Rhyme

Welcome to my zoo
Where my animals will show you what they can do...
The bear is big and furry,
If you come too close he could become scary!
The lion is yellow and lazy
But if you alarm him he goes crazy.
The monkey is small and quick,
If you offer him a banana make sure it's on a stick.
The snake is long and slithers,
If you look at him too much you get shivers!
These are the animals in my virtual zoo...
I hope you enjoyed the tour and I did not bore you!

Dylan Akash Singh (8)

Five Elms Primary School, Dagenham

Candy Land

Going to this land
Makes me hungry.
My tummy hurts after eating,
Hope we don't get banned.
Its lollipops are so big,
We need to dig underneath!
The candy is so tasty,
My bestie needs to try it!
The Skittles are so little,
We can't even see it...
I see a chocolate river
But it feels so cold, I shiver.
I don't want to go back but I have to;
Maybe I will bring a sack
And take the candy for me to share and eat!

Trisha Jannath (9)
Five Elms Primary School, Dagenham

The Land Of Infinity

In this well-known land
Historic creatures meander,
Like dinos or flies.
Though people also wander
Like Romans or Greeks,
King Arthur the Great saunters
Looking for danger
To heroically redeem his people from beasts.
A smart elephant called Hannibal the Brainy
Constantly keeps an armoured Roman on its back.
Its tummy grumbles,
But slowly begins to roar.
The Greeks have cannons
Which spit out something called Greek fire.

Moeez Musharaf (10)

Five Elms Primary School, Dagenham

The Amazing World Of Candy

Candy Land, Candy Land
All made of sweets.
Children tasting candy all day long.
Parks made of candy,
Swings made of candy.
Parents paying to go to the funfair.
Tickets made of sweets.
Rides made of sweets
Which do not last long.
Not a brick in sight.
Candy Land, Candy Land
Where sweets come from.
Children's favourite treats.
Children getting a sweet tooth from the candy.
My favourite food is candy.

Jennifer Deativo (9)
Five Elms Primary School, Dagenham

A Little Sweet Treat!

C andy is my favourite thing to eat!

A chocolate fountain is something to compete with!

N o other land is this sweet!

D idn't you know that my land is a great treat?

Y ellow, blue or green, I don't mind!

L ollipops have a great swirl

A nd my land will give a twirl!

N umber one land is just here.

D on't be afraid, we will have loads of fun!

Ruby Thomas (10)

Five Elms Primary School, Dagenham

The Minecraft Rhyme

Zombies are harsh.
Pigs are sweet.
Steak tastes good and meaty.
There is lava in caves.
There is water in the sea.
Most people love to play it
But when it's time to get off we say, "Oh no."
I've played for a day so all I can say is,
"I will play you tomorrow
And find some gold and copper."

Thai Wakeman (8)
Five Elms Primary School, Dagenham

Money Kingdom

M y awesome land is made of money

O bviously, our parents are full of lies because money does grow on trees

N ecklaces, rings and all jewellery are made of money

E xtraordinary things happen in Money Land because the land is made of money

Y es, yes, yes, if I could I would live in Money Land.

Uririoghene Naomi Eweye-Emakpose (10)
Five Elms Primary School, Dagenham

Candy City

C ome and join the fun in Candy City!

A lso gummies are hanging on a gummy tree!

N othing that tastes yuck!

D elicious things only!

Y ou better enjoy the candy!

C hocolate river falling, yum!

I t's amazing.

T asty.

Y um.

Warishah Fatima (9)

Five Elms Primary School, Dagenham

My Sister Isabella

When I met my sister
I fell in love.

She had tiny feet
And tiny toes.

With curly dark brown hair,
She was only small.

I promise I will love her every day.
We will always laugh and play.

I love you, Isabella.

Lexie Richardson (7)
Five Elms Primary School, Dagenham

Candy Craft

I crafted a world of candy,
It was so delicious.
This world I created wasn't enough.
I crafted more and more of my world.
I realised it was still not enough.
I had another idea;
If candy doesn't work, ice could.

Bhuvan Kirupaharan (10)
Five Elms Primary School, Dagenham

Candy Castle Forest

In the deepest part of the world
Where anything is possible is my candy forest,
In my world I can see...
The bubblegum people dancing beautifully
And whistling wonderfully to themselves
While the sugary green grass
Sways in the warm breeze which goes fast,
The rainbow gummy bears play who are joyful,
As the cute Skittle ladybirds bow to their subjects
In the candyfloss bushes who are loyal,
In my candy world I can hear
The liquorice trees sing with a cheer
As their marshmallow leaves baffle and sway,
While the lollipops take a snooze one day.
Far away down the path in my world you'll
discover...
The candy castle made out of Quavers
That you'll find in many different flavours,
There's a motor made of chocolate
That surrounds the candy castle,
The king and queen have a ton of parcels,

So don't come yet, they're still unwrapping you know what,
When you come remember not to take a lot,
Otherwise, they'll lose the plot,
Next to the motor is a magnificent waterfall
That dives into the motor.

Isla Houston (9)
Gidea Park Primary School, Gidea Park

Candy Land

I once had a dream
where most things were made of whipped cream.
There were cupcake cars
and picture-perfect peppermint wheels.
Also there were triple chocolate chip cookies
with popping candy hills.

There were delectable, colossal gingerbread
houses and cotton candy clouds.
When it rained luscious chocolate drops
everyone bowed.
There were fizzy rainbow belts
and liquorice bridges
and of course, it was very, very delicious.
The cookie dough sun loved hot cross buns
and in this candy land there were tons.

Also there was a short slide
and huge candy cane hand dryers
that could hold back the tide.
But then I sighed.

It was time to leave this magical world
And go back to boring old home
Where my mum and dad scream at me
in the loudest tones
but I was sure I wasn't going alone.
So I grabbed a bag knitted with strawberry laces.
Then I took everything until I knew if I took more
my belly would explode.
So please come to this wonderful place
where you will be able to stuff your face.

Abigail Ajose (9)
Gidea Park Primary School, Gidea Park

Cloudy Sea Land!

Did you know that sea creatures aren't just
from water?
And this poem I may have told to your dad's
daughter.
Well, the dolphins up there have lots of hair
And they even have a secret lair!
The dolphins on that cloud are very loud
With glasses to learn and turn.

The turtles up there eat pears in pairs.
But Postman Pat ate all the meat!
Sparkler the taunter was a lot taller
Than a stack of gold coins!
But sadly the turtles are in a terrible state.

The jellyfish up there joyfully jump
Whilst the others get into an horrendous hump.
As snappers swim in the black and blue dim,
Jellyfish jump whilst eating yummy cloud pie in
the sky.

The houses up there are wooden
And amazingly, every tool is used till it gets lost.
The metal in the kettle
Gets boiled like a bird!

The clouds up there are full of air
That fizzes and whizzes until it's froth.
Any human who dares to pass
Will fall off the land on the grass!

Jesse Goddard (8)
Gidea Park Primary School, Gidea Park

Cloud Land

I can see in my magical world,
An unusual thing to see...
A gingerbread man waving hi!
In the depths of the unknown magical sea.
Come to my world, it's a magical place.
It will definitely put a smile on your face!
There's a big cloud house floating in the blue sky
With guards waving hi at me!
But in the clouds I hear a sound!
It is a unicorn prancing around.

In my world there is lots for you to see
Like the queen with her bees.
They really do make me sneeze!
Come to my world, there is lots to see,
You'll definitely smile with glee!
Once you've travelled far enough,
You will meet a room that keeps going puff!
With a puff here and there
It is always recognised by the cloud popping fairs.

Come on, hurry up! Meet us with a grin!
In my land everything you can eat...
Nothing is impossible because...
Everything is free!

Katie Mann (8)
Gidea Park Primary School, Gidea Park

My Delectable Candy Land

In my delectable Candy Land...
There are thousands of peppermint wheels
Whirling and swirling all through the town,
The Mini Rolls are used as street lamps,
There are small houses with gummy bears
Waiting inside for a lovely warm hug.

In my delectable Candy Land...
There are Skittles as the walls, so scrumptious,
Taste the rainbow, feel the hugs.
There are rainbow Flumps, twisting
And turning on the houses frantically.
The cotton candy puffs out of the clouds
And the dough cookie sun will always be there.

In my delectable Candy Land...
There are hundreds and thousands as the stones
Which you can lick all day long,
In the Candy Land factory, gingerbread men
Work very rapidly to make succulent milkshakes
And creamy doughs for us to gobble up.

So why not come and visit this succulent place
Where every day you can stuff your face!

Mia Alger (9)
Gidea Park Primary School, Gidea Park

Kree Town

The king looked at his town
To see who was around.
He saw some citizens having some fun
And some animals eating buns.

A dragon came along and said with a grin,
"Can I join in?"
And with that,
Everyone gave him a pat.

And as the Kree
Planted a tree,
As the dragon did a dance
The cat did a prance.

The king went to inspect a house,
In there he saw a mouse
And what he did was a fright
And he took it home that very night.

When he had his new pet mouse,
He got him a little house,

In the house it had a bed
And its colour was very red.

One day the king saw a guard coloured white,
He did look quite a fright,
So to cheer him up
He gave him a pup.

The king looked at his castle
And bought a parcel,
In it, it had decorations for the door
But soon he wanted more.

George Hines (9)
Gidea Park Primary School, Gidea Park

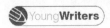

A Night-Time Adventure

I saw these little green people,
They took me out of my bed,
They flew me into a spaceship,
It was mostly red.

The ship crash-landed on an island,
It was full of candy.
The scent of ginger spread around,
Around, around and across the town.

The land had a massive river,
There were boats that were marshmallows.
Rainbow laced grass was all around,
Around, around and across the town.

Ginger houses were everywhere,
They had frosting of so many colours.
There were gummy marshmallows all around,
Around, around and across the town.

Inside the gingerbread houses there were
Little toffee tables and chairs,

Lollipop trees were all around,
Around, around and across the town.

Once the green people fixed the ship,
We went away very quick.
Luckily we got home just in time,
Just before sunrise.

Lucy Alice McDermott (8)
Gidea Park Primary School, Gidea Park

Sweet Heaven

In my sweet heaven
I would smell...
Minty candy canes straws slurping
And burping.
Chocolate river flowing and sewing.
Skittles and M&Ms moaning and groaning.
Sun heat smells like yummy pizza baking
And taking.
Slabs of chocolate melting and smelting.

In my sweet heaven
I would hear...
Candyfloss snowmen baking and hating their lives.
Marshmallow hammers smashing and bashing,
Skittle ladybugs humming.
Gummy bears chatting and burping away.
Sugar queens clapping and clicking sugar away.
Lollipops licking and sipping their lollipops.

In my sweet heaven
I would see...
Candyfloss clouds with sprinkles all over,
Minty lollipops over the sherbet grass,
Purple, pink, blue and yellow bubble gum,
Flowers everywhere.
A luxurious chocolate river flowing.
Gummy chairs jumping and bumping.

Lexi Marcou (8)
Gidea Park Primary School, Gidea Park

My Magical Land

If you hover over my magical land
You will never ever see it bland.
One of the things that you will see is an island
Which is grand!

If you hover over my magical land
You will always see the river's pink
And you will love it so much that you won't
Even want to blink!

If you hover over my magical land
You will see a little elf with striped clothes,
Big ears and wild, messy hair
And if you just turn around you will see a rose,
Beanstalk, tree right over there!

If you hover over my magical land
All of the houses are either trees or mushrooms
And every single villager likes to sit by the fire
And watch it go *boom!*

If you hover over my magical land
You will see that the sky is as colourful as a
rainbow
And once you've finished looking at everything
You are ready to go!

Evita Backyte (9)
Gidea Park Primary School, Gidea Park

In My Land

In my land, everything is sweet.
In my land, there's nothing you can't eat.
In my land, lots of things are made of candyfloss.
In my land, children are the boss.

In my land, dragons fly all day.
In my land, unicorns play.
In my land, milkshake rain drips down.
In my land, there's a candy crown.

In my land, houses are made of fudge.
In my land, no one's in a grudge.
In my land, there's a boiled sweet for a sun.
In my land, everything's fun.

In my land, candy canes and lollies grow.
In my land, there's a chocolate river that flows.
In my land, elves will wait on you.
In my land, no one gets the flu.

In my land, the weather is always calm.
In my land, jelly babies are born.

In my land, there's a chocolate tree.
In my land, no one gets stung by a bee.

Carys Hayward (8)
Gidea Park Primary School, Gidea Park

Alive Minecraft

I once had a dream where...
I heard a *click* of the game loading.
I saw a normal car *vroom* by,
But I smelt a fire torch crackling in my hand.

I once had a dream where...
I heard a crunching noise of my pixel legs.
I saw my *click* after I put my sword in my inventory,
But I smelt bread when it popped up in the hot bar.

I once had a dream where...
I heard an *umph* noise behind me.
I saw a creeper go *pppsss,* so I swung my sword.
I smelt some smoke after the creeper went *boom.*

I once had a dream where...
I heard a *ppptt* noise as I went through the temple.
I saw sand fall with a *crack.*
I smelt dust which made me cough.

I once had a dream
But now sadly it's over.

Ethan Hambleton (8)
Gidea Park Primary School, Gidea Park

Haunted Land

I can see my skeletons practising targets.
I can see the ogres being fed.
I can smell the devils drinking slime.
I can smell the orcs roasting deer.
I can feel the scales of my four-headed dragon.
I can feel my enemies' last breaths before being killed.

I can see the vampires being trapped.
I can see witches and evil wizards making new potions.
I can see werewolves trying to get the cave trolls out of the cave.
I can smell the fearful zombies' brains.
I can smell the T-rex and spinosaurus' breath.
I can feel my friends, Sonnie, Dylan and Oliver, beside me.

I can see ghosts leaving.
I can see aliens arriving
And they all bow down to... me.
George, the wolfman!

George Winser-Shead (8)
Gidea Park Primary School, Gidea Park

Easter Candy Land

In my Easter Candy Land I could see...
A bed made of marshmallow
That smelt like a strawberry.
Clouds were made of whipped cream
Floating in the bubblegum sky.
Bunnies hopped in their Easter egg trucks
And drove by.
Trees were made of ice cream cones
And peppermint leaves.

In my Easter Candy Land I could see...
Chocolate buttons were the bricks of the houses,
Tasty brown toffees were front doors,
The caramel sun showed its colour
And luscious strawberry laces were belts.

In my Easter Candy Land I could see...
Candyfloss was in tiny eggs,
Rainbow sprinkles were the rain,
Lamps were flavoured banana sweets,
Oreos were edible pavements!

Hannah Jayne Wood-Murphy (9)
Gidea Park Primary School, Gidea Park

Candy World

In my world unicorns run free,
Come to my world, there is lots to see.

Swirly pop trees turn around,
Grass is sweet so you can eat the ground,
The guard uniforms are made of candy,
Sweets are crushed to make the palace
entrance sandy.

Drink the chocolate river, it is yummy,
Have as much as you want, it won't pop
your tummy.
Candy cane walls are very hard,
They are tall like the Shard.

Chocolate wrapper limos drive on candyfloss,
But when they sink in the river they press SOS.

Sweet wrappers are cars,
The yummiest candies are kept in jars.

So come to my world there is lots to see
You can even take a replica flag which is free.

Siana Vandra (9)
Gidea Park Primary School, Gidea Park

Sugary Land

In my world, sweets are treats,
There are rivers and trees
And if you want a bite don't have a fright,
Clouds are puffy, big and fluffy,
And if you want a bite don't forget to take a flight.

Houses are made of gingerbread
And caramel crunching,
So don't have a fright just stay at night
But try not to bite.

Trees are sweet, none have leaves,
When they pop don't lop around.
They do pop in your brain
Just like a candy cane.

In a melted cottage close around,
In the hills of faraway day, a chocolate bay
Filled with chocolate when it is May.
A big overlay of chocolate flows
And in it grows a mountain rose.

Gregory Todorov (9)
Gidea Park Primary School, Gidea Park

Scientist Island

In my world there are...
Scientists who explode while some are acting abroad.
Scientists who are dancing while some are searching.
Scientists who are testing while some are playing.
Scientists who are serious and some are furious.

In my world there are...
Scientists who are crazy while some are being lazy.
Scientists who are glad while some are mad.
Scientists who are taking while some are stalking.

In my world there are...
Scientists who are fighting while some are sleeping.
Scientists who are happy while some are angry.
Scientists who are crafting while some are experimenting.
Scientists who are gasping while some are gaping.

Faizan Waseem Butt (8)
Gidea Park Primary School, Gidea Park

My Spectacular Candyland!

In my spectacular candyland...
There are cotton candy clouds,
Nearby there is a cookie dough sun
Which shines its colour over a cookie mountain.
The mountain has a path which leads you to a
chocolate river.

In my spectacular candyland...
There are gingerbread houses,
Inside there are gummy bears to cuddle,
While you sleep on marshmallow beds.
There are also doughnut chairs to sit on while
you eat.

In my spectacular candyland...
The grass that you see every day is sludge.
There are cupcake cars with peppermint wheels.
You can ride over liquorice bridges
And see ice cream trees.

Daisy Holmes (9)
Gidea Park Primary School, Gidea Park

Fantasy Land

F lying dragons in all colours of the rainbow

A mazing palaces for wizards to practise spells

N oisy witches cooking their potions

T he chocolate cupcakes hovering, ready to be caught and eaten

A nimals that can talk and eat the chocolate cupcakes

S inging trees that hum when you go by

Y awning shadows ready for a nap

L eaping spellbooks jumping onto the shelves

A mber stones glowing in the caves

N ibbling phoenixes eating their red-hot chilli

D ancing cats wearing blue top hats.

What a wonderful world,
Maybe one day you will see it too!

James Weston (9)

Gidea Park Primary School, Gidea Park

Incredible Imagination Land

In Incredible Imagination Land
Fish were swimming gracefully like a dolphin
Animals were taking selfies
Robbers were jumping out of jail
The police officers used chilli to transform into
dragons.

In Incredible Imagination Land
It was the day of Christmas
Bears got hoverboards for Christmas
Cherries were snowy cold,
You couldn't even touch them.
Snail torches were searching for sacred gems.

In Incredible Imagination Land
Sharks that fly flew in the sky.
Fantastic gymnastic dolphins did a spectacular
frontflip,
People were running on water,
Fish drank mystic water to heal themselves.

Jed Madunagu (8)
Gidea Park Primary School, Gidea Park

Snow And Ice

In my world
Everything is covered in beautiful snow,
Shimmering water frosts over
And creates shiny ice.
Everyone can skate.
If skating is not your thing,
Then look after the cute and furry animals
Or have the best snowball fight.
It is entirely up to you!
But the best thing to do is snuggle
And cuddle down with a yummy hot chocolate
Topped with colourful sprinkles,
Delicious whipped cream
And squishy marshmallows.
Wrap up warm by the fire
Or play a fun board game if you please.
You always have lots of fun!

Grace Hersey (8)
Gidea Park Primary School, Gidea Park

Candy Land

I am in this blocky world,
I saw candy everywhere.
There were marshmallow buildings,
Strawberry flavoured trees,
Popping candy grass.

I am in this blocky world,
I saw candy everywhere,
Raining gummy bears,
Melted Haribo river,
Chocolate boats.

I am in this blocky world,
I saw candy everywhere,
There were candyfloss rocks,
The axe was made of frozen jelly,
There was a chocolate fountain.

I am in this blocky world,
I saw candy everywhere,
There were candy cane cars,

There were jelly bean lights,
The paper was as delicious as chocolate.

Bradley Waddup (8)
Gidea Park Primary School, Gidea Park

Wonderland

In the deep sky where magic happens
There is an enormous castle
That makes magic chocolate.
Come and see the glowing guards' armour
And the shining sky blue
And possibly a unicorn prancing around
The candyfloss clouds.
You will also have the gingerbread men singing,
Lalalalala.
Come and get some candy lollipops.

Come to my world
And see the magical candy land of Wonderland.
You will see the queen ginger band
With a smile on her face.
You can bring as many people as you want.
Come!

Mia Josephine Moore (9)
Gidea Park Primary School, Gidea Park

My Dream

My dream...
People float in bubbles, having fun.
Houses made out of chocolate, yum!
A unicorn in disguise,
A rainbow in the sky.

My dream...
Water fountains that have melted chocolate inside.
The trees aren't just green,
They're made out of cream.
The seats are made out of marshmallow.

My dream...
The grass is made of liquorice.
The rivers are made out of chocolate.
Inside are pumpkins that are white chocolate.
Instead of apples have caramel apples.

Yasmin Cavanagh (8)
Gidea Park Primary School, Gidea Park

Candy Land!

C rumbly cookies on the floor just for you to adore

A s cute bunnies are munching on marshmallow rocks on the fishing docks

N aughty gingerbread men kicking the trees

D elightful doughnuts to start munching on

Y ummy candyfloss clouds floating in the sky

L uxurious lemonade fizzing in the spa

A mazing liquorice laces being walked on

N utella chocolate rivers coming from a choco-fall

D elicious cookie mountains which you don't need a pickaxe for.

Henry Myles-Hook (9)
Gidea Park Primary School, Gidea Park

Sweet, Sweet Candy Land

Sweet, sweet Candy Land
Candy Land is a sweet and lovely land.
You can eat, you can hear
The hot creamy chocolate trickling
While candy's tingling.

Sweet, sweet Candy Land
The green grass sways
While swirly lollipops bathe.
The gummy snakes slither
While candy canes change day and night.

Sweet, sweet Candy Land
The gummy bears dance
While the gingerbread men glance.
The candy house is sweet
With the candy rain it's such a treat.

Connor Marks-Swain (9)
Gidea Park Primary School, Gidea Park

Star Wars!

S pace battles in Star Wars Land every day.
P lanets being destroyed
A nd soldiers getting hurt.
C an one team be victorious?
E verywhere the Sith invade.

I nvaders across the galaxy.
N oisy TIE fighters and X-wings.
V ile creatures everywhere.
A steroid fields getting in the team's way.
D emolished star destroyers.
E ven wrecked planets.
R ampage across the land,
S tar Wars World is the best!

Dylan Legeai (9)
Gidea Park Primary School, Gidea Park

Music Land

When you step into this land all you will hear
Will be lovely music going through your ear.
When you step on the road it's ginormous and loud
Which will probably give you a shock
And you will jump up and down.

When you come in my land you will probably hear
Lots of playing music that will give you a cheer.
Lots of instruments are happy and glad
To see new people in their lovely land.

Instead of a clock, a triangle sings
Its favourite song, which it brings.

Bethany Norris (9)
Gidea Park Primary School, Gidea Park

Candy Polar Bear Land

Candy cane trees
Tasty and free.
Liquorice grass
Grows really fast.
Hard candy cars
Go very far.
Marshmallow polar bears
That can run funfairs.
Wafer Castle
That looks like a pastille.
Candyfloss houses
That have no mouses.
Falling marshmallows
That can fill meadows.
Lollipop sun
Tasty and yum.
Chocolate biscuit soil
That has to be in foil.
Marshmallow benches
Perfect for lunches.

White chocolate smoke
Tasty like Coke.

Reyhana Ahmed (8)
Gidea Park Primary School, Gidea Park

My Horror Land

My horror land...
The Devil's soul sit in Hell.
The shadow man lurks beneath the exit.
Will, Freddy and Bonnie are in Springlocks' fate.

My horror land...
The neighbour is setting traps.
We are making plans.
Four mannequins scattered around,
Can you find them all?
If you can come out.

My horror land...
Four pieces of cake,
Can you find them all?
Walls around the neighbour's house.
No way out,
Mwah, ha, ha!!

Christian Hayes (8)
Gidea Park Primary School, Gidea Park

Something Fishy

I can see a washing machine.
I can hear a washing machine turning.
I can feel a book in my hand.
I can see a bright light.
I can hear spring water.
I feel sleepy.
I can see sock fish swimming.
I can hear their tails swishing.
I can feel the water in my face.
I can see the underwater trees.
I can hear the trees swaying.
I can feel the water bubbling in my fingers.
I can see turtles.
I can hear the turtles swimming.
I can feel the softness of their hats.

Malachi N'lemvo (9)
Gidea Park Primary School, Gidea Park

Candy Land

In my Candy Land I can see a big, tasty lollipop.
I can hear people crunching chocolate and
lollipops.
I can feel a soft, cuddly gummy bear.
I can taste my candy in the chocolatey, amazing
pond.
I can smell all of the sweet, melting chocolate.
In my Candy Land I can see a magical candy door.
I can hear people kicking the candy grass.
I can feel the soft candyfloss cloud.
I can taste the chocolate melting in my mouth.
I can smell all of the sweet gummy bears.

Tom Atkinson (8)
Gidea Park Primary School, Gidea Park

My Caramel World

My caramel world, full of wonder,
Anime girls sing like thunder
Gummy bears scream as they're eaten a lot,
Chocolate cries as it's melted in a pot,
My caramel world, music all around,
Rap cries as it's trodden on the ground.
Anime girls and boys bravely sing,
Anime girls wear their gummy ring.
Cutting edge, amazing,
Neat, incredible, magic, endless.
My caramel world is all these things,
You probably don't want to leave.

Erica Parker-Thomson (8)
Gidea Park Primary School, Gidea Park

Cat Land

In Cat Land, everyone's a cat
But not all like to wear a hat.
The police cats chase teenagers
And a cat who blows bubbles bigger.

A grumpy cat flies to Mars
With a sign saying: 'Don't eat chocolate bars!'
In Cat Land everyone is strange
Except for one, who has had a change.

A fat cat flying in the air
And a lovely jubbly cat fair.
All the children go to school
And a skate cat who isn't cool.

James Martin (9)
Gidea Park Primary School, Gidea Park

I Had A Candy Dream

The candy trees sway
The cotton candy clouds blow
But I couldn't see any snow.

The river splashes
Tealights bang
Splash! Bang! Boom!

Come and see my world
In the corner you can see a sugar plum fairy
Waiting for me.

The sugar plum fairy prancing around,
She doesn't really care what she's around.

In my world you can hear sugar plum fairies
Whispering in my ear.

Brooke Allen (9)
Gidea Park Primary School, Gidea Park

Spectacular Candy Land!

C andy is brilliant and is tasty
A pples squirt their juicy drink
N utty, crunchy chocolate on the floor
D rink the melted chocolate
Y ou can smell the sweet scent of gingerbread

L ollies as sweet as strawberries
A big gummy bear to cuddle
N earby there is a cookie mountain
D oughnut is the yummy sun

Candy is something you will never regret.

Viren Parmar (9)
Gidea Park Primary School, Gidea Park

Dream Land

While you're awake
Your dreams are having fun.
Mario and Luigi are running
From a giant monkey.
Fairies flying, being cheeky.
Nyan Cat flying in the sky,
Leaving a rainbow trail.
Lollipops roll all over the place
And weird duck faces pop out.
Also, don't forget the cool clouds
Who guard the land.
Come to Dream Land and have some fun.

Kamile Lapuskatie (9)
Gidea Park Primary School, Gidea Park

Time To Skate

Let's start to get on the ice.
Happy to skate fast.
As the glistening ice starts to melt,
Falling on the ice, not getting hurt.
It's time for a break, get some lunch...
Time to get back on, faster and faster.
Dad says, "You're going too fast."
Time for a drink.
One more time on the ice.
Now it's time to go.

Jacob Farrell (8)
Gidea Park Primary School, Gidea Park

Candy Land

Lollipop trees fast blowing
Popping candy seeds all so mean
Chocolate mud really sticky
Marshmallow houses so tasty
Candy cane light so, so bright
Fudge mountain so, so high
Hundreds and thousands stones so, so sharp
Candyfloss smoke, *atchoo*
Easter egg maze, wow!
White chocolate snowmen, yummy
Chocolate clouds so squishy.

Kai Hindocha (8)
Gidea Park Primary School, Gidea Park

Penguin Land

When I woke up I sat up
And heard penguins singing along
To their favourite song.
They dragged me outside and I saw...
A swirly slide and penguins on the side.
An ice skating ring
And drinks going *cling*.
A hill for penguins to climb on and ride on.
A hungry stand.
A pool for penguins
And that's Penguin Land!

Roxy Ward (9)
Gidea Park Primary School, Gidea Park

Sweet Heaven

Sweet heaven
Candy Land is the best
You can eat, eat, eat until you're fit to burst.

Sweet heaven
My candy tree is filled with toffee apples,
Pears and oranges.

Sweet heaven
It always has sweets
What a treat
No water to drink
Chocolate milk to drink.

Oliver Lucas (8)
Gidea Park Primary School, Gidea Park

PS4 World

In the PS4 World
Your console will never look curled,
With Minecraft being played
Keep building your world, it will be made.

All the controllers getting used,
I am really confused.
On FIFA, if you keep scoring goals,
The most painful thing will be your soles.

Felix McKenzie Mason (9)
Gidea Park Primary School, Gidea Park

Water Park Land

In my brilliant Water Park Land
The sizzling sea water came
From the geysers and splashed everyone.
The stairs were water slides.
The people sometimes used rapids.

In my brilliant Water Park Land
We would use boats
And go down the waterfall.

Bader Muftah (8)
Gidea Park Primary School, Gidea Park

My Dear Sun Who Made Candy Land

Your glamorous land is like a superlative diamond-
encrusted pearl
With strawberry laces and mouthwatering
Cadbury's Twirls.
Your chestnut trees have lip-smacking sour treats
And ooooh! Your river is thirst-quenchingly sweet.
Your Lake Choco is a luxurious, warm drink,
Although it's meant for gazing at I kinda had a sip,
wink, wink!

Oh my great Sun, your veil shines so bright,
The opposite of your sister, Night!
It brings happy vibes along with cheerful smiles,

The colour of you is unversatile,
Above the hills, beside the blues,
Your radiant beams they shine with truth.

Your sense of love makes everything pink with
freedom,
You're so unique,
You're more beaming than a beacon.

Everybody's smiling, not a single frown,
Except from when your sister, Night
Brings out your crescent crown.
I love your land and I love you Sun,
You're not a failure,
From your loving mum,
Mother Nature.

Marvelous Daniel Ifeanyi (10)
Purfleet Primary Academy, Purfleet

Fabulous Fantasy

My land is topsy-turvy, hot and bumpy,
An underwater adventure, come and see,
You may not think of me as an underwater
creature,
I'm created you see,
The mint trees far below, are with the planets,
Sparkling like crystals.

My land is topsy-turvy,
The water splashes with a swish,
The air is swift and smooth
With multicoloured butterflies which shimmer in
the sea,
Singing their melodies,
Fish in the purple sky and seagulls in the water,
Dream up on the blanket of fluffy clouds.

Sun and moon can't wait to kiss
But they'll have to wait for the next eclipse.
The candyfloss in the sky
And the flowers so pretty and wild,
The sun is caramel and the moon is cream,
I think I'm in a fabulous fantasy.

Maia Phelut (9)
Purfleet Primary Academy, Purfleet

Candyland

In Candyland everything is sweet,
Everything you see, you can eat!

The trees are made from shiny lollipops,
And in the spring, they grow juicy pear drops.

With green liquorice fields and chocolate streams,
When the sun shines, they sparkle and gleam.

But when it rains, Skittles fall from up high,
Creating a rainbow in the sky.

That pot of gold we all look for,
Is filled with chocolate you can pour.

With fondue sticks that you can dip,
I can't help but lick my lips.

Strawberries dipped in chocolate with gold leaf,
Eating all these sweets, I'll have no teeth!

Charlotte Joanne Millard (9)
Purfleet Primary Academy, Purfleet

Imagination Land

If you look up high
You can see one of a kind, luminous colours in the sky,
Surreptitious beasts surround a castle,
While lords and merchants have a big hassle.

Unicorns and ponies run over a caramel field
While different sweets coat a tree like a shield.
The trees in this land aren't any old type
But in a stylish and beautiful stripe.

When the sun has gone down
The kings and queens put away their crowns.
The sky is filled with unending series of stars
While the sky does its own part.

The day has come,
The moonlight has gone.

Priscilla Inyang (9)
Purfleet Primary Academy, Purfleet

The Robin's Quest

One awful Christmas Day
My friend, the robin, didn't want to stay,
So he set sail and went on his way.

Across the grey, dark sky,
Robin flew so high,
All the time lightning struck he didn't bother to
sigh.

An eagle opened his jaw to bite,
It was such a frightening flight.
He still used all his might
To resist all his fright.

From sea and far away,
He landed on a stormy bay,
Robin was away,
Finally, he got home with the worst and best,
Now that's the story of the robin's quest.

Ogenna Ezeoke (9)
Purfleet Primary Academy, Purfleet

Hello Robin, Hello Home

Robin, Robin are you there?
Robin's missing his family,
Better come quick.

Crack, crack,
Twigs and sticks are snapping,
Come Mum, come Dad,
Robin's getting terrified by suspicious noises.

A white winter wonderland
Is a habitat for robins.
Robin's parents are lost in a world full of snow.

Finally,
Robin's found his parents,
A hug he needs to have,
A little kiss he needs to have,
His family he needs to have forever.

Kacey Riley (9)
Purfleet Primary Academy, Purfleet

Candy Land

Candy, candy, candy
All over the world,
Now eat some candy
And you'll never stop,
Candy, candy, candy.

Candy, candy, candy
Everyone's favourite food,
Parents don't like candy
But children love it all,
Candy, candy, candy.

Candy, candy, candy
Chocolate bears and Haribos,
Candyfloss and candy canes
Everyone loves them,
Candy, candy, candy.

Enoch Oluwatobiloba Akinwunmi-Taylor (8)
Purfleet Primary Academy, Purfleet

Candy Dream

C andy is the best treat
A land full of sweets
N ever eat vegetables here
D on't eat fruits either
Y ou will fly in Heaven

D on't forget the tasty melon
R ed, yellow, blue and green, all colours of the rainbow
E at candy, float high
A special treat just for you
M y land is as free as the ocean.

Daniella Dada (8)
Purfleet Primary Academy, Purfleet

Magic Wonderland

M agic tricks are fun

A ll the fairies come to Magic School

G inormous Easter eggs are our snack

I learn new spells every day

C ats can ride on broomsticks.

W e shoot magic stars out of our wands

O n Saturdays, we ride our unicorns

N early touching the sky

D ogs magically talk in Wonderland

E ven the unicorns have something to say!

R abbits riding on a roller coaster

L uckily the tooth fairy comes here for holidays

A ction-packed broomstick games are the best

N othing is better than riding a broomstick

D efinitely, this is the best place to be.

Ellen Mitchell (8)
Silver End Academy, Silver End

Sliver End Land

S ilky green land

I n houses that are grand,

L iving here is great,

V ery fun with no hate,

E veryone is friendly,

R eally nice, especially Wendy.

E ndless fun to have,

N ight-time clubs with Gav

D aytime at school with Mr Row.

A ll the people say,

C ome to mine to stay.

A fter school we play,

D arkness doesn't keep us away.

E very day we learn,

M aths makes our brains burn,

Y ou will love it here, I promise my dear.

Harmony Nicola Jane West (10)
Silver End Academy, Silver End

Friendship Never Melts Away

A friend is someone you have a bond with
And mutual affection.
We don't always get it right, nothing's perfection.
We all want a friend that we can trust and like
Sure there will be times you might fight
But you'll be there for each other
Through the good and the bad.
Sometimes happiness and the sad,
So always value your friend
And hope the friendship never ends.
As you are mine and I am yours
Our friendship has opened too many doors.
True friends are hard to find,
If they're anything like you, they're one of a kind.

Tyler Howlett (10)
Silver End Academy, Silver End

Drumstick Island

The streets are made of peanut brittle
The trees are made of chocolate
The leaves are made of French fries and burgers
What a wonderful place to live

Everything's made of sweets or fast food
No savoury food in sight
Everyone loves Drumstick Island
Especially at night

The stars are bright and colourful
The moon is made from cheese
The sky at night is wonderful
No clouds or fog in sight

I love Drumstick Island, it's the place to go
When everyone is asleep and silent.

Grace Aspinall (10)
Silver End Academy, Silver End

Upside-Down Land

Three little aliens lived in a town,
It was so topsy-turvy it was upside down.

These aliens walked by,
Their heads, not their feet,
They scared everybody that lived down their street.

There were no people to see or animals too,
It was sad as the aliens had no one to say boo!

There was no car, but spaceships to drive,
It was too hard for them as they only had arms of
five.

Yeah, but the best thing of all
The upside-down houses looked very small.

Christopher Stephens (11)
Silver End Academy, Silver End

Magic Dream

Oh magic, magic are you real?
Do you ever wonder what magic is like?
Come to my land and we'll explore.
There is a band in a stand,
It plays music magically,
Let's dance with the fairies, unicorns and trolls,
Our feet will move to the magical beat.
We will sparkle from our head to our feet,
The moon comes out like a glitter globe
And that's when we start our disco mode.
The stars will shine, shimmer and gleam.
I hope I never wake up from this dream.

Harriet Keeble (8)

Silver End Academy, Silver End

Musical, Foody, Sporty, Halloween Nightmare

One horrifying night,
Scary food came into sight.
A young boy who loved rugby,
Thought he was very funny.
Nightmares struck,
He decided to duck.
As food runs to the forest,
People call them Boris.
Science proves this is impossible,
People think it's plausible.
When they came they danced to music,
He runs away because he loses it.
They dive underwater,
He only finds a quarter.
This poem ends with magic,
All was very tragic.

Marcus John Harris (9)
Silver End Academy, Silver End

Land Of Rainbows

In the Land of Rainbows,
All kinds of magic goes.
The rainbow is made of candy
And when you're hungry it's very handy.

Sparkle is a unicorn,
She has magic in her horn.
She loves to laugh and loves to play,
She loves to dance around and sing all day.

The parties here are crazy,
We all jump on giant daisies,
Everyone here has a sparkling glow
In the Land of Rainbows.

Lia Reed (10)
Silver End Academy, Silver End

Candyland Dream

Funny dancing frog,
Yummy chocolate log,
It all tastes nice,
Chocolate sprinkles in ice.

The trees are red and white,
You could just take a bite,
There's even a caramel lake,
Eat as much as you can take.

The grass is green,
All made of buttercream,
A candyland extreme,
Where you can live a dream.

Caitlyn Turner (11)
Silver End Academy, Silver End

Birthdays

B irthdays are for celebrating
I t is a time to spend with friends and family
R emembering others is important
T rifles and treats and other sweets
H appy times for making happy memories
D ancing and games is such fun
A lways looking forward to the next one
Y early birthdays.

Megan Walker (11)
Silver End Academy, Silver End

Mythical Land

M ermaids swimming in the sea
Y etis licking ice lollies
T rolls giggle under the bridge
H igh in the sky hovers a dragon
I can see what you can't
C an you see the unicorns in the forest?
A ll the animals are not in the zoo
L augh along with me while we go and see.

Lola Rees-Tearle (9)

Silver End Academy, Silver End

My Dream Garden

P henomenal flowers
H anging vines
E legant leaves
N atural springs
O utstanding waters
M agical bushes
E nchanting skies
N utritious apples
A mazing clouds
L umpy rocks.

Jasmin Perkins (11)

Silver End Academy, Silver End

The Land Of Animals

A magical place

N othing but animals

I have been there in my dreams

M ajestic and mysterious

A ll who visit will love it

L ost in time and space

S afe from all danger.

Lewis Plumer (9)

Silver End Academy, Silver End

The Game Over The Hill

G o to the Hill of Games today

A wesome adventures coming your way from over the hill and far away

M ad games to play all day

E verlasting fun, hooray.

Max Moore (8)

Silver End Academy, Silver End

YoungWriters Est. 1991

YOUNG WRITERS INFORMATION

We hope you have enjoyed reading this book – and that you will continue to in the coming years.

If you're a young writer who enjoys reading and creative writing, or the parent of an enthusiastic poet or story writer, do visit our website **www.youngwriters.co.uk**. Here you will find free competitions, workshops and games, as well as recommended reads, a poetry glossary and our blog.

If you would like to order further copies of this book, or any of our other titles, then please give us a call or visit **www.youngwriters.co.uk**.

Young Writers
Remus House
Coltsfoot Drive
Peterborough
PE2 9BF
(01733) 890066
info@youngwriters.co.uk